Help with Homework

Multiplying and Dividing

How to use this book with your child:

It is recommended that an adult spends time with a child while doing any kind of school practice, to offer encouragement and guidance. Find a quiet place to work, preferably at a table, and encourage your child to hold his or her pen or pencil correctly.

Try to work at your child's pace and avoid spending too long on any one page or activity. Most of all, emphasise the fun element of what you are doing and enjoy this special and exciting time!

Don't forget to add your reward sticker to each page you complete!

Reward
sticker!

Designed by Plum5
Illustrations by Sue King, Sharon Smart and Andy Geeson
Educational consultant Josh Levenson and Nina Filipek

Autumn
Publishing

Multiplication tables 1 - 6

Complete the multiplication tables below.
Try to learn them off by heart.

x1

1 x 1 = 1

2 x 1 = 2

3 x 1 = 3

4 x 1 = 4

5 x 1 = 5

6 x 1 = ☐

7 x 1 = 7

8 x 1 = 8

9 x 1 = 9

10 x 1 = ☐

11 x 1 = 11

12 x 1 = 12

x2

1 x 2 = 2

2 x 2 = 4

3 x 2 = 6

4 x 2 = ☐

5 x 2 = 10

6 x 2 = 12

7 x 2 = 14

8 x 2 = 16

9 x 2 = 18

10 x 2 = 20

11 x 2 = 22

12 x 2 = ☐

x3

1 x 3 = 3

2 x 3 = 6

3 x 3 = 9

4 x 3 = ☐

5 x 3 = 15

6 x 3 = 18

7 x 3 = 21

8 x 3 = ☐

9 x 3 = 27

10 x 3 = 30

11 x 3 = 33

12 x 3 = 36

x4

1 x 4 = 4

2 x 4 = 8

3 x 4 = 12

4 x 4 = 16

5 x 4 = ☐

6 x 4 = 24

7 x 4 = 28

8 x 4 = 32

9 x 4 = ☐

10 x 4 = 40

11 x 4 = 44

12 x 4 = 48

x5

1 x 5 = 5

2 x 5 = 10

3 x 5 = 15

4 x 5 = 20

5 x 5 = ☐

6 x 5 = 30

7 x 5 = 35

8 x 5 = 40

9 x 5 = 45

10 x 5 = ☐

11 x 5 = 55

12 x 5 = 60

x6

1 x 6 = 6

2 x 6 = ☐

3 x 6 = 18

4 x 6 = 24

5 x 6 = 30

6 x 6 = 36

7 x 6 = 42

8 x 6 = 48

9 x 6 = ☐

10 x 6 = 60

11 x 6 = 66

12 x 6 = 72

Reward sticker!

Multiplication tables 7 – 12

Complete the multiplication tables below.
Try to learn them off by heart.

×7

1 x 7 = ☐
2 x 7 = 14
3 x 7 = 21
4 x 7 = 28
5 x 7 = 35
6 x 7 = ☐
7 x 7 = 49
8 x 7 = 56
9 x 7 = 63
10 x 7 = 70
11 x 7 = 77
12 x 7 = 84

×8

1 x 8 = 8
2 x 8 = 16
3 x 8 = 24
4 x 8 = 32
5 x 8 = 40
6 x 8 = 48
7 x 8 = ☐
8 x 8 = 64
9 x 8 = 72
10 x 8 = ☐
11 x 8 = 88
12 x 8 = 96

×9

1 x 9 = 9
2 x 9 = 18
3 x 9 = 27
4 x 9 = 36
5 x 9 = ☐
6 x 9 = 54
7 x 9 = 63
8 x 9 = 72
9 x 9 = ☐
10 x 9 = 90
11 x 9 = 99
12 x 9 = 108

Reward sticker!

x10

1 x 10 = 10

2 x 10 = 20

3 x 10 = 30

4 x 10 = ☐

5 x 10 = 50

6 x 10 = 60

7 x 10 = 70

8 x 10 = 80

9 x 10 = 90

10 x 10 = ☐

11 x 10 = 110

12 x 10 = 120

x11

1 x 11 = 11

2 x 11 = 22

3 x 11 = 33

4 x 11 = ☐

5 x 11 = 55

6 x 11 = 66

7 x 11 = 77

8 x 11 = 88

9 x 11 = ☐

10 x 11 = 110

11 x 11 = 121

12 x 11 = 132

x12

1 x 12 = 12

2 x 12 = ☐

3 x 12 = 36

4 x 12 = 48

5 x 12 = 60

6 x 12 = ☐

7 x 12 = 84

8 x 12 = 96

9 x 12 = 108

10 x 12 = 120

11 x 12 = 132

12 x 12 = 144

Reward sticker!

Multiplication problems

Solve these multiplication problems and write your answers in the boxes.

a. 4 × 2 =   11 × 2 =

b. 6 bicycles have 2 wheels each. How many wheels are there altogether?

c. 3 × 5 =   9 × 5 =

d. 7 houses have 5 windows each. How many windows are there altogether?

e. 5 × 10 =   8 × 10 =

f. 12 children have 10 fingers each. How many fingers are there altogether?

Reward sticker!

g. 5 × 3 = [ ]   11 × 3 = [ ]

h. **7** tricycles have **3** wheels each. How many wheels are there altogether? [ ]

i. 7 × 4 = [ ]   9 × 4 = [ ]

j. **12** ladybirds have **4** spots each. How many spots are there altogether? [ ]

k. 4 × 6 = [ ]   11 × 6 = [ ]

l. **8** rabbits each eat **6** carrots. How many carrots have the rabbits eaten altogether? [ ]

Alien multiplication

Solve these alien multiplication problems and write your answers in the boxes.

a. **8** x **7** = ☐   **3** x **7** = ☐

b. **11** aliens have **7** arms each. How many arms are there altogether?  ☐

c. **8** x **8** = ☐   **6** x **8** = ☐

d. **12** aliens have **8** toes each. How many toes are there altogether? ☐

e. **9** x **9** = ☐   **6** x **9** = ☐

f. **4** aliens have **9** eyes each. How many eyes are there altogether? ☐

Reward sticker!

What's the answer?

Solve these multiplication problems and write your answers in the boxes.

a. 7 × 11 = ☐   12 × 11 = ☐

b. 4 × 11 = ☐   8 × 11 = ☐

c. There are **11** football players in a team and there are **6** teams. How many football players are there altogether? ☐

d. 4 × 12 = ☐   9 × 12 = ☐

e. 7 × 12 = ☐   3 × 12 = ☐

f. **8** girls have **12** sweets each. How many sweets are there altogether? ☐

Reward sticker!

Square numbers

A square number is a number which is multiplied by itself.
e.g. The **square of 2** is the same as **2 x 2**.
Solve these square numbers and write your answers in the boxes.

7 x 7 = ☐   1 x 1 = ☐

12 x 12 = ☐   4 x 4 = ☐

9 x 9 = ☐   2 x 2 = ☐

3 x 3 = ☐   10 x 10 = ☐

8 x 8 = ☐   5 x 5 = ☐

6 x 6 = ☐   11 x 11 = ☐

Challenge: Put the square numbers above in order, lowest to highest.

_____ _____ _____ _____ _____

_____ _____ _____ _____ _____

What do you notice about the difference (the gap)
between each of the square numbers above?

_____ _____ _____ _____ _____

Reward
sticker!

_____ _____ _____ _____ _____

Short multiplication

Practise multiplying a two digit number by a one digit number.
Use the space to show your workings.

e.g. **17 × 4 =** 68

```
    1 7
  ×   4
  -----
    6 8
    2
```

21 × 4 =

32 × 3 =

19 × 5 =

13 × 6 =

12 × 7 =

More short multiplication

Practise multiplying a two digit number by a one digit number. Use the space to show your workings.

e.g. **34 × 5 =** | **170**

```
      3 4
  ×     5
  -------
    1 7 0
      2
```

29 × 4 =

38 × 3 =

53 × 5 =

42 × 6 =

17 × 7 =

Reward sticker!

Opposites and inverse

Using the multiplications below, work out the inverses (divisions).
Don't forget, you need to use all of the same numbers!

e.g. **3 x 5 = 15** so **15 ÷ 3 = 5**
or **15 ÷ 5 = 3**

a. 3 x 4 = 12 so ☐ ÷ ☐ = ☐

b. 5 x 6 = 30 so ☐ ÷ ☐ = ☐

c. 4 x 7 = 28 so ☐ ÷ ☐ = ☐

d. 11 x 9 = 99 so ☐ ÷ ☐ = ☐

Reward
sticker!

13

Multiplication facts

Using the example, work out the multiplications below.
Write your answers in the boxes.
What do you notice?

e.g.   **2 x 3 = 6** so **20 x 3 = 60**

5 x 4 = 20 so **50 x 4 =**

9 x 5 = 45 so **90 x 5 =**

7 x 8 = 56 so **70 x 8 =**

6 x 7 = 42 so **6 x 70 =**

Reward sticker!

$3 \times 7 = 21$ so $30 \times 7 =$

$4 \times 6 = 24$ so $4 \times 60 =$

$7 \times 9 = 63$ so $70 \times 9 =$

and $70 \times 90 =$

$11 \times 8 = 88$ so $110 \times 8 =$

and $110 \times 80 =$

Test time!

Are you ready to test yourself? Have a go at these questions and see how many you get right!

a. 2 x 2 = [ ]   **b.** 5 x 8 = [ ]

c. 4 x 5 = [ ]   **d.** 6 x 7 = [ ]

e. 8 x 8 = [ ]   **f.** 11 x 2 = [ ]

g. 1 x 3 = [ ]   **h.** 10 x 11 = [ ]

i. 13 children have **3** toys each. How many toys are there altogether? [ ]

j. What is the square of **3**? [ ]

k. What is the square of **9**? [ ]

Reward sticker!

16

l. 60 × 5 = ☐

m. 43 × 4 = ☐

n. 52 × 3 = ☐

o. 37 × 5 = ☐

p. 8 × 3 = 24 so 80 × 3 = ☐

q. 11 × 11 = 121 so 11 × 110 = ☐

r. and 110 × 110 = ☐

Reward
sticker!

Division tables 1 – 6

Complete the division tables below.
Try to learn them off by heart.

÷1

1 ÷ 1 = 1

2 ÷ 1 = 2

3 ÷ 1 = 3

4 ÷ 1 = 4

5 ÷ 1 = 5

6 ÷ 1 = ☐

7 ÷ 1 = 7

8 ÷ 1 = 8

9 ÷ 1 = 9

10 ÷ 1 = 10

11 ÷ 1 = ☐

12 ÷ 1 = 12

÷2

2 ÷ 2 = 1

4 ÷ 2 = 2

6 ÷ 2 = 3

8 ÷ 2 = ☐

10 ÷ 2 = 5

12 ÷ 2 = 6

14 ÷ 2 = 7

16 ÷ 2 = 8

☐ ÷ 2 = 9

20 ÷ 2 = 10

22 ÷ 2 = 11

24 ÷ 2 = 12

÷3

3 ÷ 3 = 1

6 ÷ 3 = 2

9 ÷ 3 = 3

12 ÷ 3 = ☐

15 ÷ 3 = 5

18 ÷ 3 = 6

21 ÷ 3 = 7

24 ÷ 3 = 8

☐ ÷ 3 = 9

30 ÷ 3 = 10

33 ÷ 3 = 11

36 ÷ 3 = 12

Reward sticker!

÷4

$4 \div 4 = 1$

$8 \div 4 = 2$

$12 \div 4 = 3$

$16 \div 4 = \boxed{}$

$20 \div 4 = 5$

$24 \div 4 = 6$

$28 \div 4 = 7$

$\boxed{} \div 4 = 8$

$36 \div 4 = 9$

$40 \div 4 = 10$

$44 \div 4 = 11$

$48 \div 4 = 12$

÷5

$5 \div 5 = 1$

$10 \div 5 = 2$

$15 \div 5 = 3$

$20 \div 5 = 4$

$25 \div 5 = 5$

$\boxed{} \div 5 = 6$

$35 \div 5 = 7$

$40 \div 5 = \boxed{}$

$45 \div 5 = 9$

$50 \div 5 = 10$

$55 \div 5 = 11$

$60 \div 5 = 12$

÷6

$6 \div 6 = 1$

$12 \div 6 = 2$

$\boxed{} \div 6 = 3$

$24 \div 6 = 4$

$30 \div 6 = 5$

$36 \div 6 = 6$

$42 \div 6 = 7$

$48 \div 6 = 8$

$54 \div 6 = \boxed{}$

$60 \div 6 = 10$

$66 \div 6 = 11$

$72 \div 6 = 12$

Reward sticker!

Division tables 7 - 12

Complete the division tables below.
Try to learn them off by heart.

÷7

7 ÷ 7 = 1

14 ÷ 7 = 2

☐ ÷ 7 = 3

28 ÷ 7 = 4

35 ÷ 7 = 5

42 ÷ 7 = ☐

49 ÷ 7 = 7

56 ÷ 7 = 8

63 ÷ 7 = 9

70 ÷ 7 = 10

77 ÷ 7 = 11

84 ÷ 7 = 12

÷8

8 ÷ 8 = 1

16 ÷ 8 = 2

24 ÷ 8 = 3

32 ÷ 8 = 4

40 ÷ 8 = ☐

48 ÷ 8 = 6

56 ÷ 8 = 7

64 ÷ 8 = 8

72 ÷ 8 = 9

80 ÷ 8 = 10

88 ÷ 8 = 11

☐ ÷ 8 = 12

÷9

9 ÷ 9 = 1

18 ÷ 9 = 2

27 ÷ 9 = 3

36 ÷ 9 = 4

45 ÷ 9 = 5

54 ÷ 9 = ☐

63 ÷ 9 = 7

72 ÷ 9 = 8

☐ ÷ 9 = 9

90 ÷ 9 = 10

99 ÷ 9 = 11

108 ÷ 9 = 12

Reward
sticker!

÷10

10 ÷ 10 = 1

20 ÷ 10 = 2

30 ÷ 10 = 3

☐ ÷ 10 = 4

50 ÷ 10 = 5

60 ÷ 10 = 6

70 ÷ 10 = 7

80 ÷ 10 = ☐

90 ÷ 10 = 9

100 ÷ 10 = 10

110 ÷ 10 = 11

120 ÷ 10 = 12

÷11

11 ÷ 11 = 1

22 ÷ 11 = 2

33 ÷ 11 = 3

44 ÷ 11 = 4

55 ÷ 11 = ☐

66 ÷ 11 = 6

77 ÷ 11 = 7

88 ÷ 11 = 8

☐ ÷ 11 = 9

110 ÷ 11 = 10

121 ÷ 11 = 11

132 ÷ 11 = 12

÷12

12 ÷ 12 = 1

24 ÷ 12 = 2

36 ÷ 12 = ☐

48 ÷ 12 = 4

60 ÷ 12 = 5

72 ÷ 12 = 6

84 ÷ 12 = 7

☐ ÷ 12 = 8

108 ÷ 12 = 9

120 ÷ 12 = 10

132 ÷ 12 = 11

144 ÷ 12 = 12

Reward sticker!

Division precision

Solve these dividing problems and write your answers in the boxes.

a. 8 ÷ 2 = [ ]   14 ÷ 2 = [ ]

b. Share **12** books equally [ ]
between **2** children.
How many books each?

c. 15 ÷ 5 = [ ]   40 ÷ 5 = [ ]

d. Share **35** carrots equally [ ]
between **5** rabbits.
How many carrots each?

e. 50 ÷ 10 = [ ]   80 ÷ 10 = [ ]

f. Share **120** bananas equally
between **10** monkeys. How
many bananas each?

 [ ]

Reward
sticker!

22

g. 12 ÷ 3 = ☐   21 ÷ 3 = ☐

h. Share **18** balloons equally between **3** clowns. How many balloons each? ☐

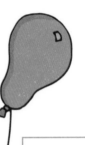

i. 12 ÷ 4 = ☐   40 ÷ 4 = ☐

j. Share **36** acorns equally between **4** squirrels. How many acorns each? ☐

k. 54 ÷ 6 = ☐   48 ÷ 6 = ☐

l. Share **72** berries equally between **6** birds. How many berries each? ☐

Division problems

Solve these division problems and write your answers in the boxes.

a. **28 ÷ 7 =** ☐   **56 ÷ 7 =** ☐

b. Share **84** biscuits equally between **7** children. How many biscuits each? ☐

c. **16 ÷ 8 =** ☐   **64 ÷ 8 =** ☐

d. Share **72** apples equally between **8** horses. How many apples each? ☐

e. **54 ÷ 9 =** ☐   **72 ÷ 9 =** ☐

f. Share **63** stickers equally between **9** boys. How many stickers does each boy have? ☐

Reward sticker!

g. 132 ÷ 11 = ☐   77 ÷ 11 = ☐

h. 99 ÷ 11 = ☐   33 ÷ 11 = ☐

i. **121** football players are split equally into **11** teams. How many players are there in each team? ☐

j. 48 ÷ 12 = ☐   96 ÷ 12 = ☐

k. 72 ÷ 12 = ☐   36 ÷ 12 = ☐

l. Share **60** bees equally between **12** beehives. How many bees in each? ☐

Reward sticker!

25

Fact attack!

Using the example, work out these division problems.
Write your answers in the boxes.

e.g. $35 \div 5 = 7$ SO $350 \div 5 = 70$

$50 \div 5 = 10$ SO $500 \div 5 =$ ☐

$45 \div 5 = 9$ SO $450 \div 5 =$ ☐

$8 \div 2 = 4$ SO $80 \div 2 =$ ☐

$15 \div 3 = 5$ SO $150 \div 3 =$ ☐

Reward sticker!

$48 \div 12 = 4$ so $480 \div 12 =$ ☐

$21 \div 7 = 3$ so $210 \div 7 =$ ☐

$70 \div 10 = 7$ so $700 \div 10 =$ ☐

and $700 \div 100 =$ ☐

$54 \div 9 = 6$ so $540 \div 9 =$ ☐

and $540 \div 90 =$ ☐

Short division

Practise dividing a two digit number by a one digit number.
Use the space to show your workings.

e.g. **72 ÷ 6 =** | **12** | **45 ÷ 5 =**

```
        1  2
   ┌─────────
 6 │ 7 ¹2
```

99 ÷ 9 =

77 ÷ 7 =

Share **58** sweets between **8** children.

How many sweets
does each child get?

How many sweets
are left over?

Test time!

Are you ready to **test yourself**? Have a go at these questions and see how many you can get right!

a. 6 ÷ 3 =

b. 64 ÷ 8 =

c. 14 ÷ 2 =

d. 40 ÷ 4 =

e. 25 ÷ 5 =

f. 5 ÷ 5 =

g. 27 ÷ 9 =

h. 21 ÷ 3 =

i. Share **44** books equally between **11** boys. How many books each?

j. Share **39** carrots equally between **7** rabbits. How many carrots each?

k. How many carrots are left over?

Reward sticker!

29

Test time 2!

$20 \div 5 = 4$ so $200 \div 5 =$ ☐

$72 \div 9 = 8$ so $720 \div 9 =$ ☐

 and $720 \div 90 =$ ☐

$88 \div 8 =$ ☐

$90 \div 10 =$ ☐

$84 \div 7 =$ ☐

$25 \div 5 =$ ☐

Reward sticker!

Answers

Multiplication tables

6 x 1 = **6**		10 x 1 = **10**
4 x 2 = **8**		12 x 2 = **24**
4 x 3 = **12**		8 x 3 = **24**
5 x 4 = **20**		9 x 4 = **36**
5 x 5 = **25**		10 x 5 = **50**
2 x 6 = **12**		9 x 6 = **54**
1 x 7 = **7**		6 x 7 = **42**
7 x 8 = **56**		10 x 8 = **80**
5 x 9 = **45**		9 x 9 = **81**
4 x 10 = **40**		10 x 10 = **100**
4 x 11 = **44**		9 x 11 = **99**
2 x 12 = **24**		6 x 12 = **72**

Multiplication problems

a. 4 x 2 = **8**   11 x 2 = **22**

b. **12** wheels

c. 3 x 5 = **15**   9 x 5 = **45**

d. **35** windows

e. 5 x 10 = **50**   8 x 10 = **80**

f. **120** fingers

g. 5 x 3 = **15**   11 x 3 = **33**

h. **21** wheels

i. 7 x 4 = **28**   9 x 4 = **36**

j. **48** spots

k. 4 x 6 = **24**   11 x 6 = **66**

l. **48** carrots

Alien multiplication

a. 8 x 7 = **56**   3 x 7 = **21**

b. **77** arms

c. 8 x 8 = **64**   6 x 8 = **48**

d. **96** toes

e. 9 x 9 = **81**   6 x 9 = **54**

f. **36** eyes

What's the answer?

a. 7 x 11 = **77**   12 x 11 = **132**

b. 4 x 11 = **44**   8 x 11 = **88**

c. **66** football players

d. 4 x 12 = **48**   9 x 12 = **108**

e. 7 x 12 = **84**   3 x 12 = **36**

f. **96** sweets

Square numbers

7 x 7 = **49**		1 x 1 = **1**
12 x 12 = **144**		4 x 4 = **16**
9 x 9 = **81**		2 x 2 = **4**
3 x 3 = **9**		10 x 10 = **100**
8 x 8 = **64**		5 x 5 = **25**
6 x 6 = **36**		11 x 11 = **121**

Challenge **1, 4, 9, 16, 25, 36, 49, 64, 81, 100, 121, 144**

The gaps increase by **3, 5, 7, 9, 11, 13, 15, 17, 19, 21, 23**

Short multiplication

21 x 4 = **84**

32 x 3 = **96**

19 x 5 = **95**

13 x 6 = **78**

12 x 7 = **84**

More short multiplication

29 x 4 = **116**

38 x 3 = **114**

53 x 5 = **265**

42 x 6 = **252**

17 x 7 = **119**

Opposites and inverse

a. 12 ÷ 3 = **4**   or   12 ÷ 4 = **3**

b. 30 ÷ 5 = **6**   or   30 ÷ 6 = **5**

c. 28 ÷ 4 = **7**   or   28 ÷ 7 = **4**

d. 99 ÷ 9 = **11**   or   99 ÷ 11 = **9**

Answers

Multiplication facts

50 x 4 = **200**

90 x 5 = **450**

70 x 8 = **560**

6 x 70 = **420**

30 x 7 = **210**

4 x 60 = **240**

70 x 9 = **630**

70 x 90 = **6,300**

110 x 8 = **880**

110 x 80 = **8,800**

Test time!

a. 2 x 2 = **4**

b. 5 x 8 = **40**

c. 4 x 5 = **20**

d. 6 x 7 = **42**

e. 8 x 8 = **64**

f. 11 x 2 = **22**

g. 1 x 3 = **3**

h. 10 x 11 = **110**

i. **39** toys

j. **9**

k. **81**

l. **300**

m. **172**

n. **156**

o. **185**

p. 80 x 30 = **240**

q. 11 x 110 = **1,210**

r. 110 x 110 = **12,100**

Division tables

6 ÷ 1 = **6**   11 ÷ 1 = **11**

8 ÷ 2 = **4**   18 ÷ 2 = **9**

12 ÷ 3 = **4**   27 ÷ 3 = **9**

16 ÷ 4 = **4**   32 ÷ 4 = **8**

30 ÷ 5 = **6**   40 ÷ 5 = **8**

18 ÷ 6 = **3**   54 ÷ 6 = **9**

---

21 ÷ 7 = **3**   42 ÷ 7 = **6**

40 ÷ 8 = **5**   96 ÷ 8 = **12**

54 ÷ 9 = **6**   81 ÷ 9 = **9**

40 ÷ 10 = **4**   80 ÷ 10 = **8**

55 ÷ 11 = **5**   99 ÷ 11 = **9**

36 ÷ 12 = **3**   96 ÷ 12 = **8**

Division precision

a. 8 ÷ 2 = **4**   14 ÷ 2 = **7**

b. **6** books

c. 15 ÷ 5 = **3**   40 ÷ 5 = **8**

d. **7** carrots

e. 50 ÷ 10 = **5**   80 ÷ 10 = **8**

f. **12** bananas

g. 12 ÷ 3 = **4**   21 ÷ 3 = **7**

h. **6** balloons

i. 12 ÷ 4 = **3**   40 ÷ 4 = **10**

j. **9** acorns

k. 54 ÷ 6 = **9**   48 ÷ 6 = **8**

l. **12** berries

Division problems

a. 28 ÷ 7 = **4**   56 ÷ 7 = **8**

b. **12** biscuits

c. 16 ÷ 8 = **2**   64 ÷ 8 = **8**

d. **9** apples

e. 54 ÷ 9 = **6**   72 ÷ 9 = **8**

f. **7** stickers

g. 132 ÷ 11 = **12**   77 ÷ 11 = **7**

h. 99 ÷ 11 = **9**   33 ÷ 11 = **3**

i. **11** players

j. 48 ÷ 12 = **4**   96 ÷ 12 = **8**

k. 72 ÷ 12 = **6**   36 ÷ 12 = **3**

l. **5** bees

Fact attack!

500 ÷ 5 = **100**

450 ÷ 5 = **90**

80 ÷ 2 = **40**

150 ÷ 3 = **50**

480 ÷ 12 = **40**

210 ÷ 7 = **30**

700 ÷ 10 = **70**

700 ÷ 100 = **7**

540 ÷ 9 = **60**

540 ÷ 90 = **6**

Short division

45 ÷ 5 = **9**

99 ÷ 9 = **11**

77 ÷ 7 = **11**

7 sweets each

2 sweets left over

Test time!

a. 6 ÷ 3 = **2**

b. 64 ÷ 8 = **8**

c. 14 ÷ 2 = **7**

d. 40 ÷ 4 = **10**

e. 25 ÷ 5 = **5**

f. 5 ÷ 5 = **1**

g. 27 ÷ 9 = **3**

h. 21 ÷ 3 = **7**

i. **4** books

j. **5** carrots each

k. **4** carrots left over

Test time 2!

200 ÷ 5 = **40**

720 ÷ 9 = **80**

720 ÷ 90 = **8**

88 ÷ 8 = **11**

90 ÷ 10 = **9**

84 ÷ 7 = **12**

25 ÷ 5 = **5**